Printed and published by D.C. Thomson & Co., Ltd., 185 Fleet Street, London EC4A 2HS.
© D.C. Thomson & Co., Ltd., 1985.
**ISBN** 0 85116 347 5

## It's a lucky draw—

## But not for Paw

# hen it comes to telling fibs—

## There's no one like His Nibs!

# There's a special place for Hen—

## Down at the But 'n' Ben

This restaurant is affy posh—

But when Paw treats the folks—oh, gosh!

*Daph or Maggie? Which will it be?—*

*You're going to chuckle when you se*

# Michty me! Whit affy shocks—

## Lie behind that letter-box!

A dripping tap? A pipe that's burst?—

This drip-drip makes Paw fear the worst!

# *Daph's blind date—*

## *Sounds really great!*

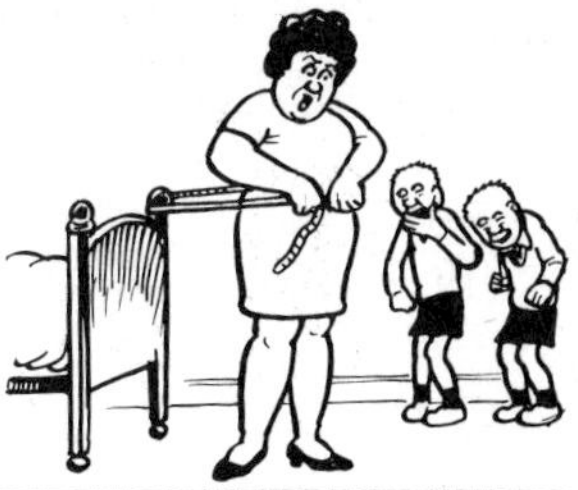

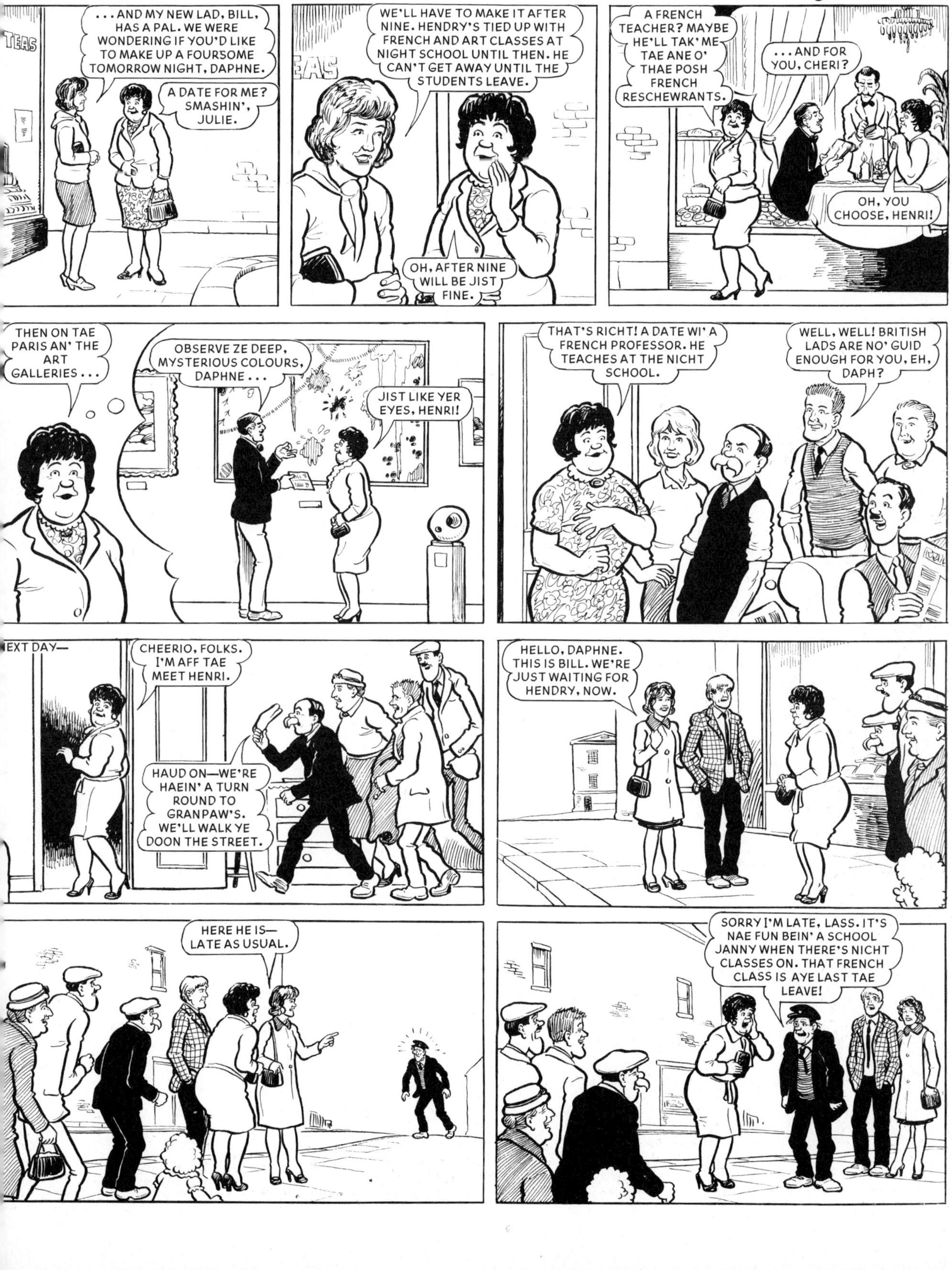

## There's something fishy going on here—

## When the lassies' posters disappear!

## Ha-ha, Broon sheep . . . !

elp m'boab! What a to-do—

## All because of a big ACHOO!

# o wonder Gran'paw wears a grin—

## He's cured the Broons o' buttin' in!

ichty me! Well-well-well—

*If it isn't auld walrus-face himsel'!*

# Mighty me! Here's a funny scene—

## Wi' a bent-up Broon on the boolin' green!

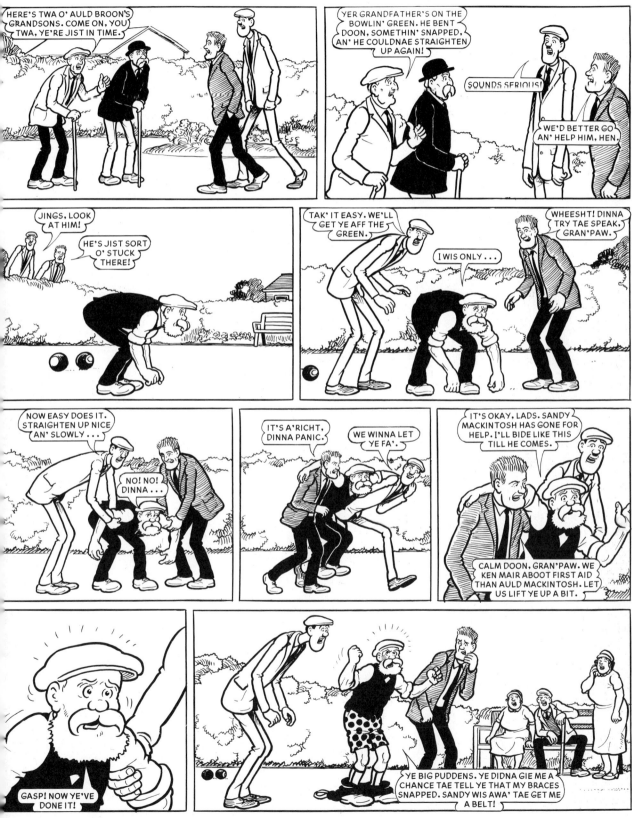

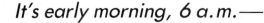

# Poor Paw's in a proper tizz—

## He doesn't know what day it is!

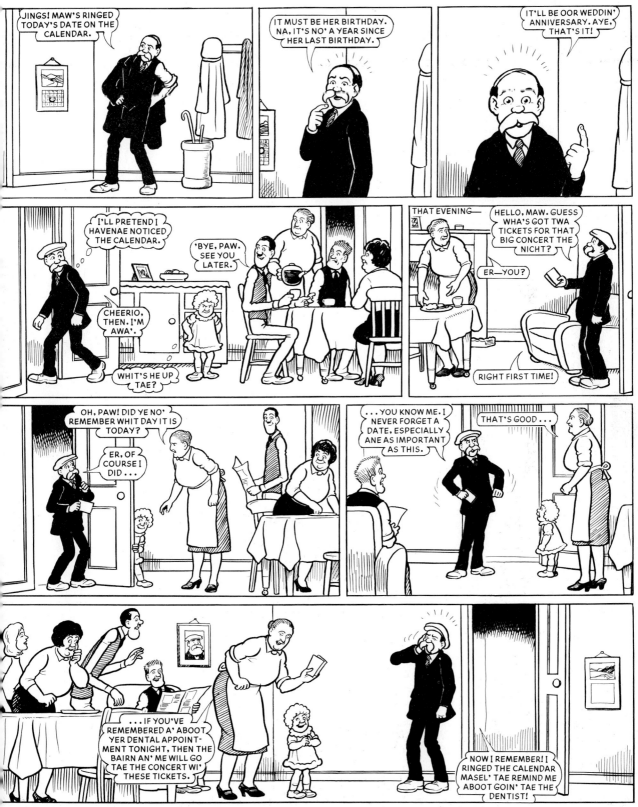

# Who's the mystery telephone user?—

## Whoever it is, Paw Broon's the loser

*Guess which Broon—*

*Quietens Hamish doon!*

# Gran'paw's tough, Gran'paw's hearty—

## Gran'paw's also very crafty

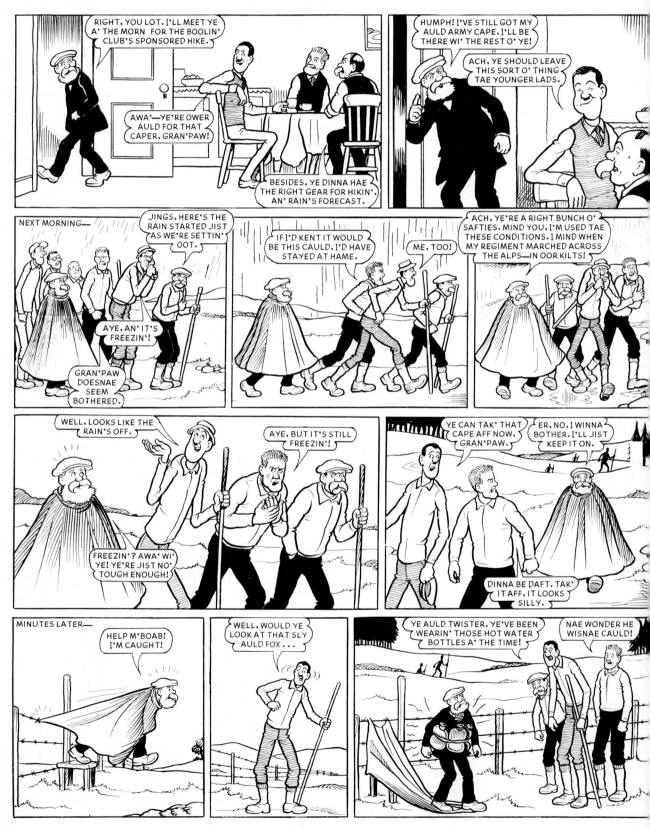

ainting by numbers? Jings, that's fun—

And it gets the decorating done!

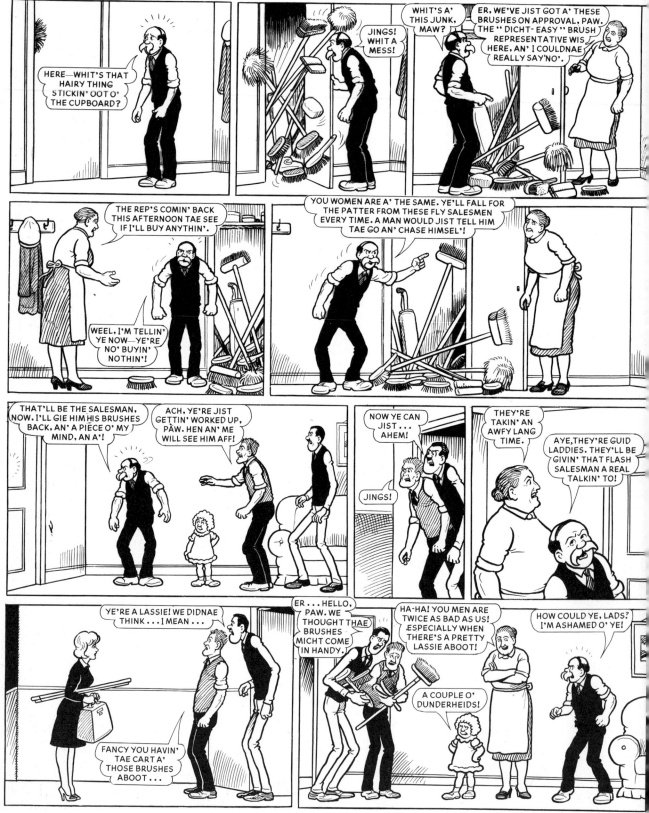

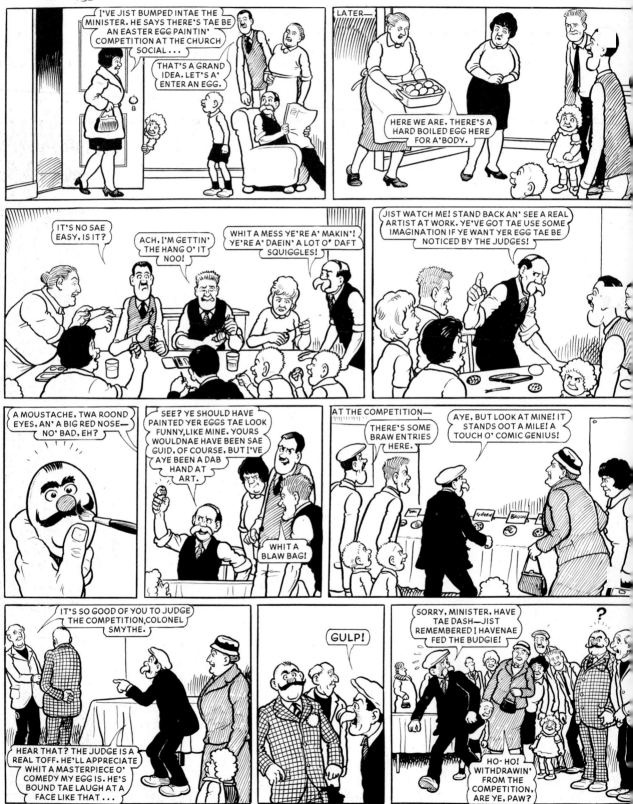

ere's the oddest thing ye've ever seen—

Horace's special TV "screen"!

*here's trouble in store—*

## *From the new lad next door!*

Monsieur Broon thinks he's jist great—

But see whit turns up on his plate!

*'s a very funny sight indeed—*

*When they go to work full speed!*

# Help m'boab! Whit a caper—

## When poor Paw tries to read his paper

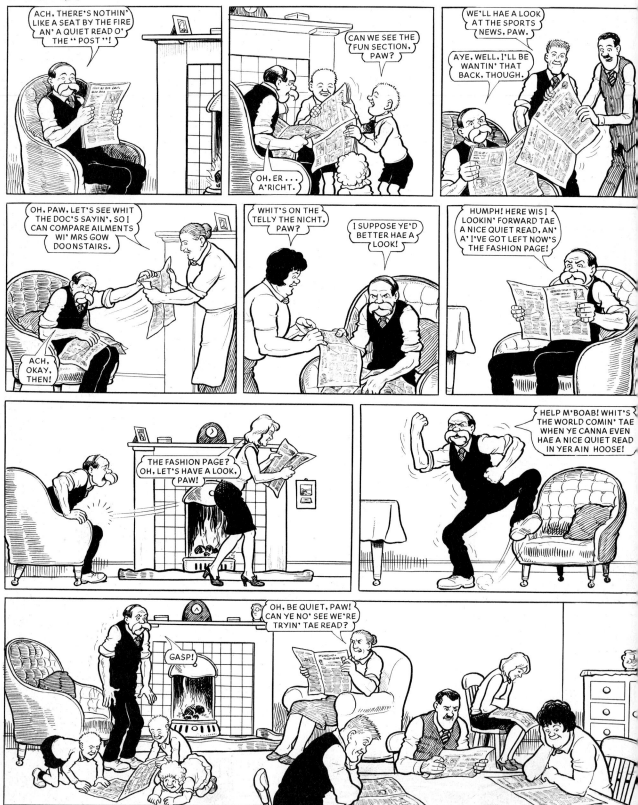

No tea, no telly, no ticking clock—

And then there comes an affy shock!

# This "Easter bonnet" for the Bairn—

## Is like the one her pals are wearin'

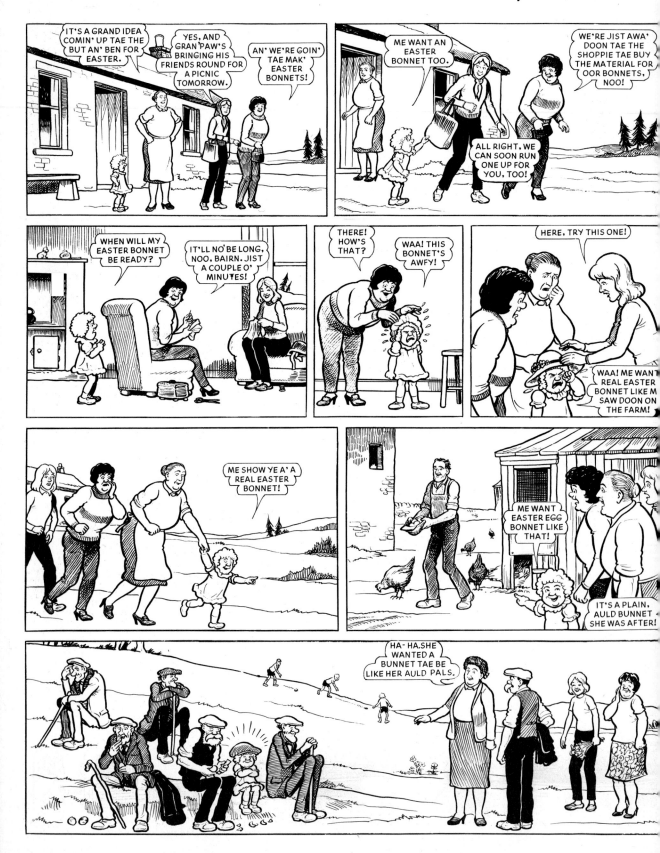

*Michty me! Whit consternation—*

*When they all want their favourite station*

*Nae wonder Paw groans wi' despair—*

*This carnival is just "no' fair!".*

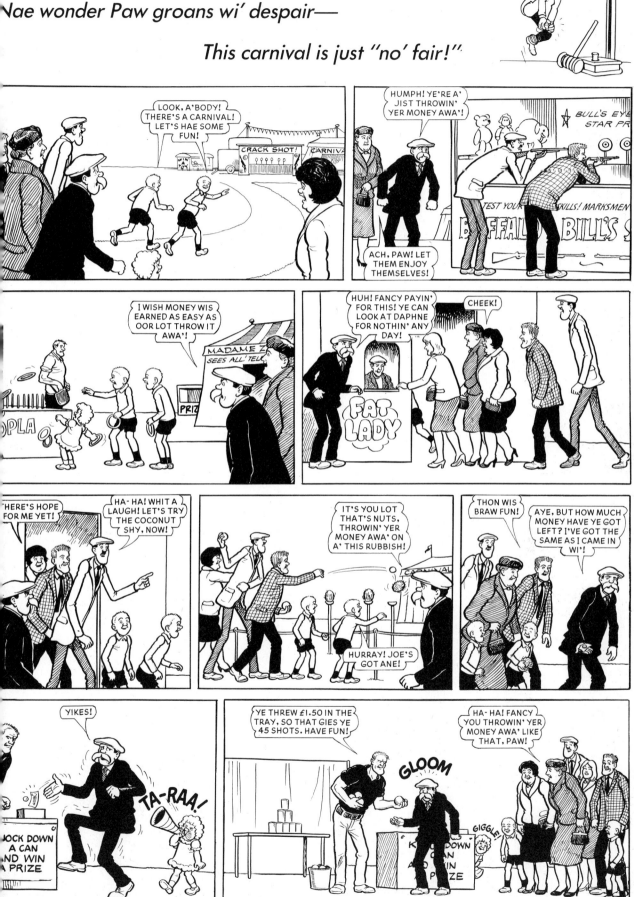

# Risotto? Curry? Paw's had enough!—

## He canna stand this fancy stuff

## . . But Maw and Daph—

### Have the last laugh!

# Nae wonder Paw Broon's woebegone—

## Here's a proper CARRY-on!

# Jings, what a shock—

## Gran'paw likes "rock'

*he Broons all think they're affy posh—*

*Till Paw bends doon, and then—oh gosh!*

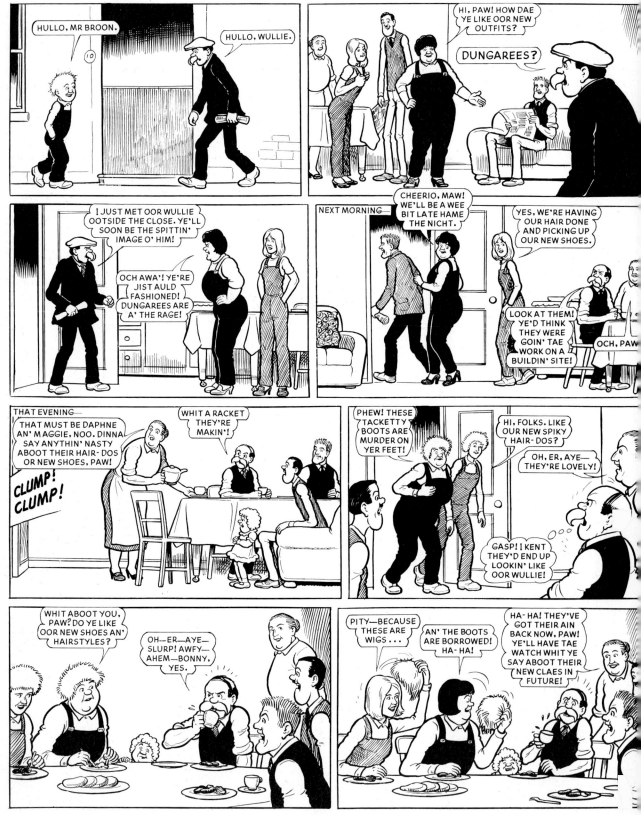

Paw's oot o' luck! Trust him to find—

Micro chips of EVERY kind!

# TV's banned, and that is that!—

## But there's still a lot to goggle at

**AN EVENING AT NO. 10—**

WELL, WELL, AN' WHIT HAVE YOU A' BEEN DAEIN' THE DAY?

NO REPLY!

THIS TELEVISION IS KILLIN' OFF ALL CONVERSATION IN THIS HOOSE! THERE'S PLENTY O' OTHER THINGS YE COULD DAE, RATHER THAN WATCH THIS!

AW, MAW!

MAGGIE! DAPHNE! YOU COULD BE DAEIN' THE WASHIN'! THAT'S FAR MAIR IMPORTANT THAN THE TELLY!

AYE, OKAY, MAW.

COME ON! WE'LL CLEAN OOT THE FISH BOWL.

AYE, IT'S FELL MUCKY.

MUCKY? THE PUIR WEE FISHIE CAN HARDLY SEE OOT!

WE CAN PUT A PLUG ON THE DIGITAL CLOCK, THEN, JOE.

AYE, IT'S BEEN LYIN' ABOOT UNUSED SINCE WE GOT IT AT CHRISTMAS!

I'LL JUST HAE A QUIET SMOKE BY THE FIRE.

**LATER—**

WELL, HOW ARE YE A' GETTIN' ON, THEN?

ENGROSSED!

HELP M'BOAB! I GIVE UP!

FASCINATED!

DREAMIN'!

## Paw and Gran'paw get big shocks—

## Now they're really on the rocks

A giant, gruesome, hairy bat—

Who on earth is scared o' that

When things get moved aboot!

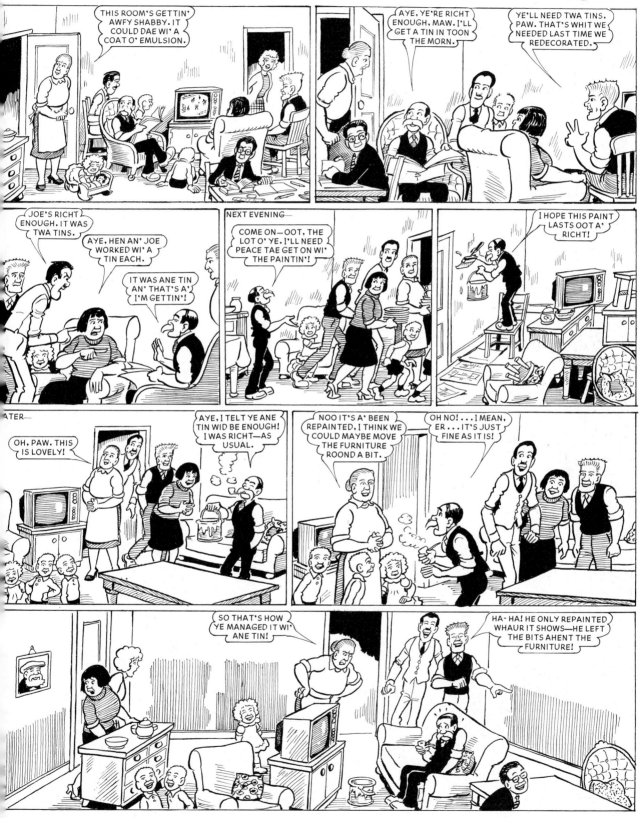

# There's trouble galore—

## With a four-legged mowe

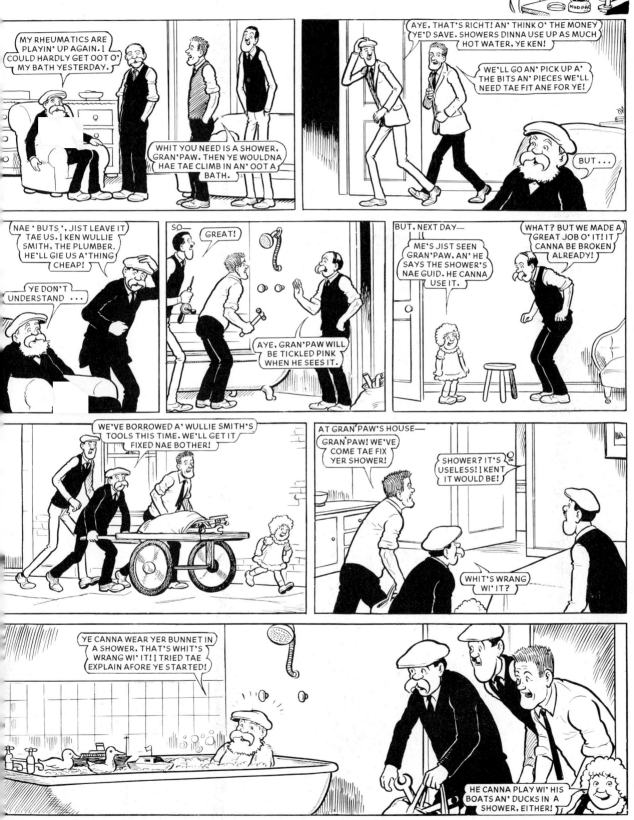

he Broons are all in fancy dress—

And what is Daph? Ye'll never guess!

What a surprise—

## From the tatties Paw buys!

## *When Daph hears folk talking!*

# Twenty-four candles, burning bright—

## Is Daphne thrilled to bits? No' quite!

# Tam's no' quite such a toff—

## When his jacket comes off.

One wheel that's big, one wheel that's small—

It seems that Gran'paw's sure to fall.

# Fit tae run, fit tae hike?—

## Hen Broon's fit tae drop, mair like

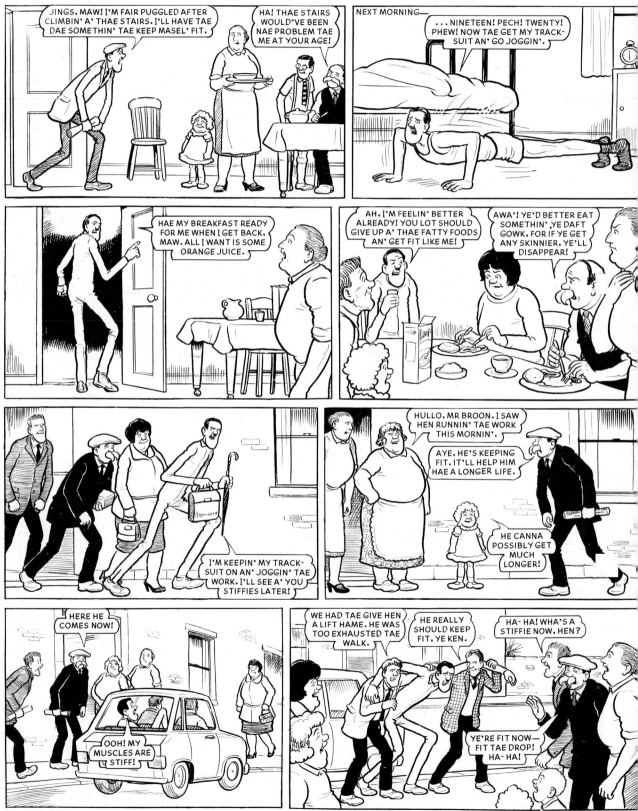

*. . . but Paw Broon didn't think he'd find—*

*"Skinheads" of another kind*

When Paw Broon plans a hike!

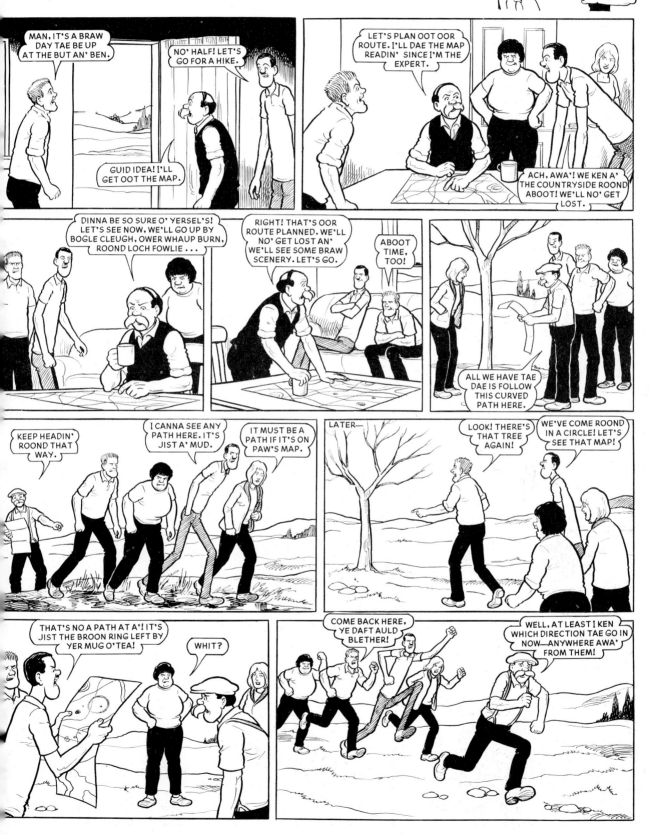

## About who wears what!

wing high, swing low—

Swing ho-ho-ho!

*No wonder Paw is feeling ill—*

*Guess what's on the window-si*

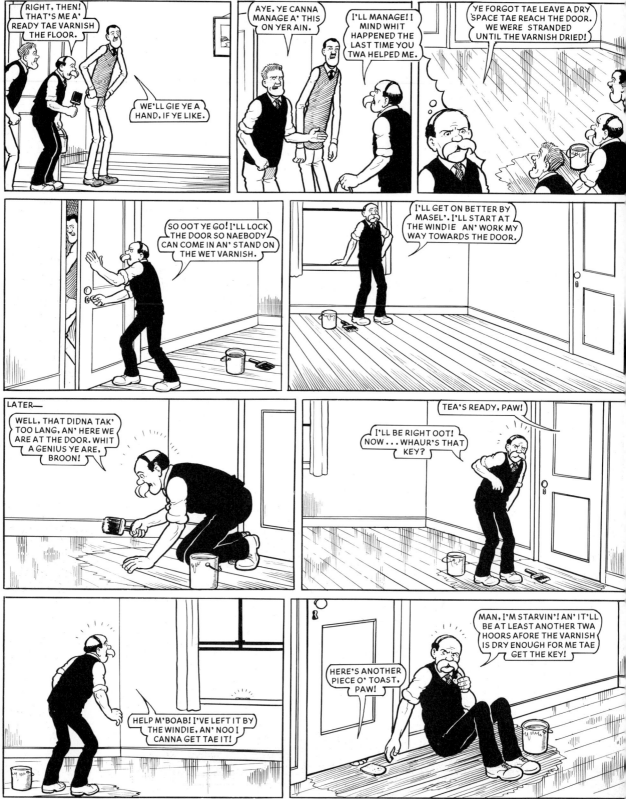

A *stuffy, noisy atmosphere?*—

*You wouldn't think you'd find that HERE!*

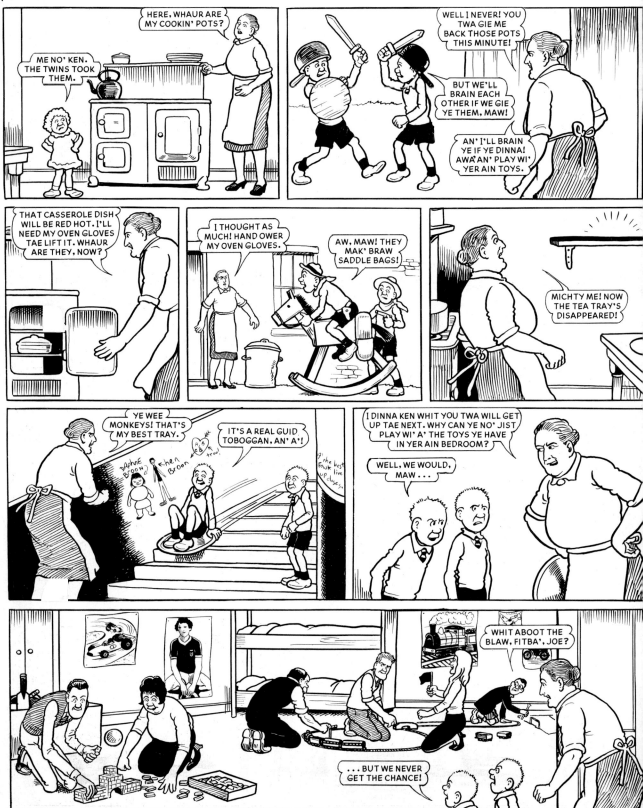

What a din! Oh, my gosh—

These rugby fans are not so posh!

# Nothing to puff—

## Puts Paw in the huff

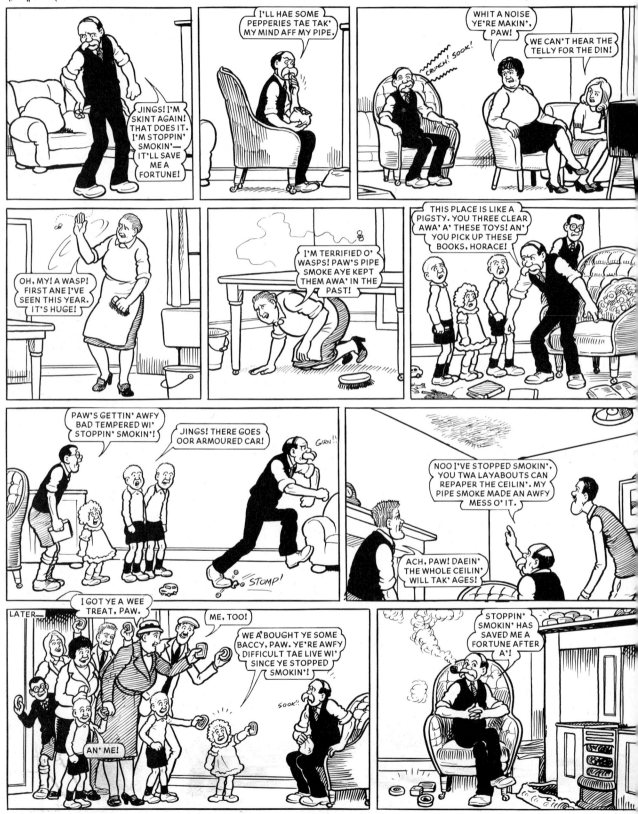

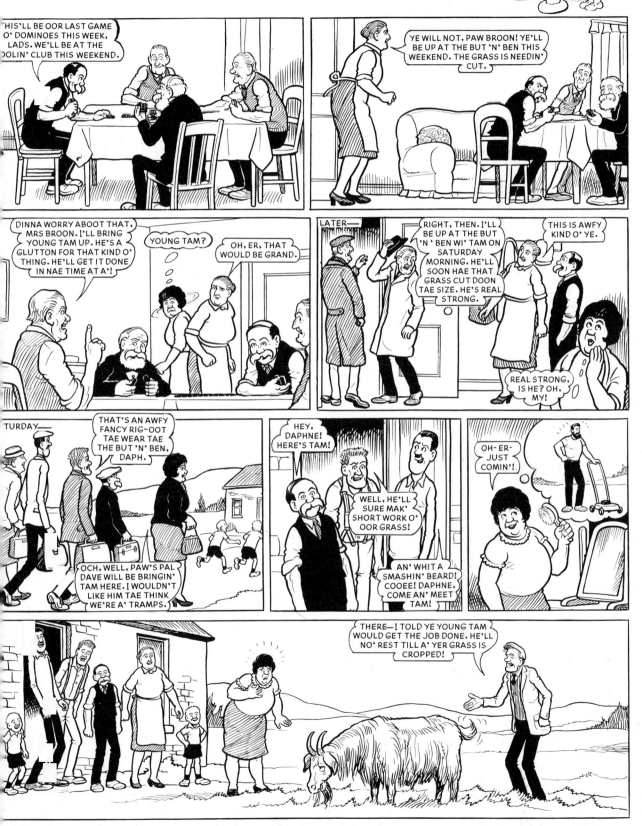

here's a shock for oor lass—

## When Tam cuts the grass!